Georgia HALL

TRINITY
GUILDHALL

Piano Grade 2
Pieces & Exercises
for Trinity Guildhall examinations

2009-2011

Published by:
Trinity College London
89 Albert Embankment
London SE1 7TP UK

T +44 (0)20 7820 6100
F +44 (0)20 7820 6161
E music@trinityguildhall.co.uk
www.trinityguildhall.co.uk

Printed in England by Halstan & Co. Ltd, Amersham, Bucks.

Gavotte

George Frideric Handel
(1685–1759)

Dynamics are editorial.
The left hand crotchets may be lightly detached.

Air: des trois fermiers

Félix-Louis Despréaux
(1748–1820)

Dynamics and phrasing are editorial.

Study in F

no. 17 from *25 Elementary Studies*, op. 176

Jean-Baptiste Duvernoy
(1802–1880)

Sicilienne

Charles Koechlin
(1867–1950)

(1) The right hand takes over the tied note.

Study no. 21

from *Etudes for Piano,* op. 47

Alexander Goedicke
(1877–1957)

Children's Song

from *For Children, SZ 42*

Béla Bartók
(1881–1945)

Metronome mark is composer's own.

Lied (song)

from *Let's Build a Town*

Paul Hindemith
(1895–1963)

Dynamics are editorial and have been added for examination purposes only.

Oxford Rag

Alan Bullard
(born 1947)

With intelligence, and not too fast [♩ = 112–126]

Song without Words

John Kember

Exercises

1a. I Wish

Tempo lento, un poco rubato [♩ = c. 63]

1b. Medieval Mood

precise ♩♪
press to the bottom of the key

Smoothly [♩ = c. 88]

QUIET

hold 5th

count!

2a. Go to the Superstore ✓

Allegretto (optional 'swing-feel') [♩ = c. 116]

2b. Mountain Echo

3a. Gathering Strength

3b. Up Hill, Down Dale

D MAJOR scale (together — forte or piano)

R	1	2	3	1	2	3	4	1	2	3	1	2	3	4	5
	D	E	F#	G	A	B	C#	D	E	F#	G	A	B	C#	D	
L	5	4	3	2	1	3	2	1	4	3	2	1	3	2	1	

Bb MAJOR scale ✳

R	2	1	2	3	1	2	3	4	1	2	3	1	2	3	4
	Bb	C	D	Eb	F	G	A	Bb	C	D	Eb	F	G	A	Bb
L	3	2	1	4	3	2	1	3	2	1	4	3	2	1	3

G minor scale

R	1	2	3	1	2	3	4	1	2	3	1	2	3	4	5
	G	A	Bb	C	D	Eb	F#	G	A	Bb	C	D	Eb	F#	G
L	5	4	3	2	1	3	2	1	4	3	2	1	3	2	1

B minor scale

R	1	2	3	1	2	3	4	1	2	3	1	2	3	4	5
	B	C#	D	E	F#	G	A#	B	C#	D	E	F#	G	A#	B
L	4	3	2	1	4	3	2	1	3	2	1	4	3	2	1

Chromatic scale on Bb (together — forte or piano)

Play every note. Always 3rd on black notes

D MAJOR arpeggio (separate) *mf*

R	1	2	3	1	2	3	5
	D	F#	A	D	F#	A	D
L	5	3	2	1	3	2	1

Bb MAJOR arpeggio ✳

R	2	1	2	4	1	2	4
	Bb	D	F	Bb	D	F	Bb
L	3	2	1	3	2	1	3

G minor arpeggio

R	1	2	3	1	2	3	5
	G	Bb	D	G	Bb	D	G
L	5	3	2	1	3	2	1

B minor arpeggio

R	1	2	3	1	2	3	5
	B	D	F#	B	D	F#	B
L	5	3	2	1	3	2	1